grade
2

For full details of exam requir
current syllabus in conjun
Information & Regulations and
teachers and parents, *These*
documents are available onl
well as free of charge from m
local representatives or from
The Associated Board of the Royal Schools of Music,
24 Portland Place, London W1B 1LU, United Kingdom.

C000098723

CONTENTS

Where appropriate, pieces in this album have been checked with original source material
and edited as necessary for instructional purposes. Fingering, bowing, composers'
metronome marks and the editorial realization of ornaments (where given) are for
guidance only; they are not comprehensive or obligatory. Metronome marks within square
brackets are suggested for exam purposes and need not be strictly observed.

Violin consultant: Edward Huws Jones
Footnotes: Edward Huws Jones (EHJ) and Anthony Burton

**DO NOT
PHOTOCOPY
© MUSIC**

Alternative pieces for this grade

Music origination by Barnes Music Engraving Ltd
Cover by Økvik Design
Printed in England by Caligraving Ltd, Thetford, Norfolk

Rondo

Third movement from Duo in D, Op. 8 No. 5

Arranged by
Friedrich Hermann

I. J. PLEYEL

Ignace Joseph Pleyel (1757–1831) was an Austrian-born pupil of Joseph Haydn who enjoyed great success in Paris as composer, publisher and piano manufacturer. This is the last movement of one of a set of six 'Little Duos' for two violins, of gradually increasing difficulty, which he published himself as his Opus 8 in 1806, and which was soon rapidly reprinted all over Europe. This arrangement by the German violinist and composer Friedrich Hermann (1828–1907) is for violin and piano. The original second violin part can be found in the right hand of the piano part, and you might enjoy trying to work out how it went and playing the movement with a violinist friend. The movement is called Rondo, which usually indicates that the main tune comes back several times in alternation with contrasting 'episodes'. Here there is only one episode, in the minor key, and only the first part of the main tune is repeated before the 'coda' or tail-piece. In bb. 42–3, the lower note of each chord is optional.

AB 3277

Kemp's Jig

A:2

Arranged by
Edward Huws Jones

ANON.

Will Kemp was a celebrated Elizabethan actor and a member of Shakespeare's own company. He was a great comedian and prankster and in 1600 he danced from London to Norwich – a distance of over a hundred miles – for a bet. *Kemp's Jig*, which is arranged here from the original version for solo lute, celebrates this feat. This extrovert piece calls for a lively two-in-a-bar pulse. EHJ

Rigaudon

Arranged by
Paul de Keyser and Fanny Waterman

RAMEAU

Jean-Philippe Rameau (1683–1764) was the leading French composer at the time of J. S. Bach and Handel. This Rigaudon is in his collection of *Pièces de clavecin*, or 'Pieces for harpsichord', published in 1724. A rigaudon is a French dance of folk origin. Despite the time signature here, it should have the feeling of two rather than four beats to the bar.

Moon River

B:1

MANCINI and MERCER

Henry Mancini (1924–94) was a famous American composer and conductor of film scores. You probably know his theme tune for *The Pink Panther*, and you may also have heard this number, which comes from the 1961 film *Breakfast at Tiffany's* and won an Oscar that year for Best Song. The title *Moon River* fits the first three notes. The words of the song (by Johnny Mercer) are about dreaming of something 'waiting round the bend', and once you're sure of the rhythms you could try to suggest that dreamy quality by playing more freely than you would in a classical piece.

B:2

Fröhlicher Landmann

No. 10 from *Album für die Jugend*, Op. 68

Arranged by
Edward Huws Jones

SCHUMANN

Fröhlicher Landmann The Jolly Farmer; **Album für die Jugend** Album for the Young

This was originally a piano piece, written for Schumann's *Album for the Young* in 1848. Schumann gave the melody to the left hand of the piano (his jolly farmer was a baritone!) and in this arrangement it needs a rich, warm tone with lots of bow. EHJ

The Boys of Wexford

B:3

Arranged by
William Alwyn

TRAD. IRISH

The Associated Board has been carrying out exams and publishing pieces for them for a long time now, and this arrangement of a traditional revolutionary song from southern Ireland was included in the syllabus in 1927. At the time, its arranger William Alwyn (1905–85) was a young musician earning his living as a flautist and teacher, but he went on to become a well-known composer of both film scores and concert music. This arrangement brings out the lyrical quality of the melody, which calls for generous bow strokes and a singing tone.

© 1927 by The Associated Board of The R. A. M. and The R. C. M.

Reproduced from *First Violin*, Book II (ABRSM Publishing)

for Adam, Anastasia and Seneaih

Cossacks

No. 20 from *Shooting Stars*

KATHERINE and HUGH COLLEDGE

Husband-and-wife team Kathy (b. 1952) and Hugh (b. 1945) Colledge both worked as instrumental music teachers in East London before moving to Norfolk in 1995. Their compositions and arrangements are a joint effort, with Kathy being the string specialist and Hugh writing the piano accompaniments. This piece comes from a collection called *Shooting Stars*, written 'for the string players at St Angela's Ursuline Convent School, Forest Gate, London Borough of Newham'. The Cossacks were famous fighters on horseback from the more remote regions of the old Russian empire, though the title here refers not to their riding skills but to cossacks energetic and exuberant dancing.

Through My Window

C:2

Arranged by
Timothy Kraemer

TRAD. HUNGARIAN

This arrangement of a Hungarian folksong comes from a volume called *Gypsy Jazz*, designed, the editors say, to give young players 'the opportunity to travel horizons beyond "classical" music and thus discover a world of traditional songs and dances'. In the song, 'the abandoned maiden bemoans her fate, looking through her window at the moon'. The instruction *parlando* means 'speaking', and is applied to a kind of folk singing closely following the rhythms and stresses of Hungarian speech – for example, the short–long rhythms in bb. 6 and 13. You could try to bring out the difference between this and the more rhythmic, dance-like style of the *Faster* sections.

Caribbean Sunshine

No. 33 from *Fiddle Time Runners*

KATHY and DAVID BLACKWELL

The 'Caribbean sunshine' in this piece comes from the syncopated rhythms associated with the calypso – originally a Trinidadian song with improvised words commenting on topics of the day. The composers, Kathy and David Blackwell, both studied music at Edinburgh University, and now live in Oxfordshire. They work respectively as an instrumental teacher and in music publishing, and also enjoy writing tunes for string players.